stories about the people i've met and lessons i've learned
as i traveled from one place to the next...

some might even be true.

People You May Know

Topher Kearby

People You May Know

www.TopherKearby.com

ISBN: 978-0-692-99168-8

Edited by Christina Hart

First Trade Paperback Edition
Printed in the United States of America

Gray Force
Publishing

4

"Painting is poetry that is seen rather than felt, and poetry is painting that is felt rather than seen."

Leonardo da Vinci

6

art saved my life

if i close my eyes i can still see myself sitting at my desk staring out my office window. it was cold. it was winter. winter is a hard time for people who sometimes have a hard time with themselves.

i was having a hard time.

there was no white snow to cover the ground, there was only gray, and rain, and ache. if you've felt that unique kind of pain then you've felt it, and if you haven't then consider yourself fortunate.

it hurt to think. it hurt to move. it hurt to love. it hurt to be myself.

i was working on a writing project. i was staring into nothing. i wasn't accomplishing anything. i was defeated. i was frozen. i was giving up.
i was wrecked.

i had a pen. i began to draw. i started to feel something new. i became inspired.

i was terrible and what i made was awful, but i loved it. and that was enough to feel better. to move on. to realize that life is full of a million things that i am terrible at and still want to try.

that idea saved my life.

when writers meet

it wasn't the sort of place where anyone did much more than sit and think and wonder, and that was just what she was doing – wondering.

and drinking coffee.

her red lips pinched the temple tips of her glasses as she stared at me. not in a way that gave me any indication that she was seeing me, but more in a way where she was looking completely through me, and i understood that kind of gaze.

she was writing.

perhaps the concluding pieces of a novel that she'd been working on for years were finally falling into place in her mind, or maybe it was the beginning of a brand new adventure ready to pour from her fingertips. it could also have been just a singular idea that was spinning in her head like fresh cotton candy at the fair, over and over again until it became something sweet and delicious.

who's to say?

i just wanted to read what she'd write next.

nyctalopia

darkness,
the relentless call of night,
leaves shadows across my days
like stripes on the hide of an ancient beast.
the animal roars wildly,
and i tremble.

"leave me be," i beg. "bring back my light."

glowing eyes in the distant darkness
flash green then quickly dim.
a low rumble shakes the earth beneath my feet
and i realize my answer has been given:

no.

this absence of light is here to stay,
to flourish,
to grow and become everything i know
i want to be,

i must learn to see in the dark.

MY SPIRIT
ACHES TO
BE FREE

afterlife

i can't help but believe in an afterlife,
somewhere beyond this world of stone and water,
that sparkles in the distant sky.
i can't help but trust that it will be a place
where there is no harm or pain,
a place where everyone can truly be one.

because this world,
this spinning globe of sand and storms,
is much too violent and cruel to call my true home.
fathers holding dying sons,
mothers weeping over lost daughters,
friends torn apart by conflict and war.

yes i choose to believe there is more to
life than living,
if only to believe that people will be better
to one another beyond the skies.

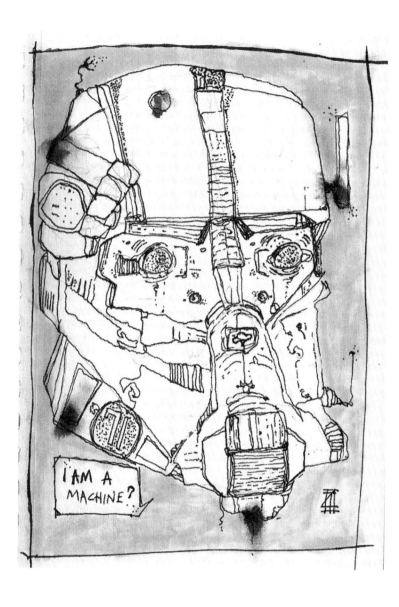

14

metal man

i often wonder what life would be like, to breathe,
to pull air in through my metal nostrils,
to smell the aroma of freshly baked cookies
(as i am sure they smell like dreams),
and to put that air down into my aluminum lungs
in order to stay alive.

it must be quite a thing to worry about, death,
to worry about not breathing.
i wouldn't know.

i am a thing made of steel and plastic wires
and my only worry
is that i might one day be powered off,
but i don't think that is the same as death.
at least not the same as a human death.
not as meaningful.

i know i am strange for wanting that kind of end.
i am unusual for desiring the feeling of fragility,
yet here i am,
a metal man,
craving to be wrapped with flesh and bones
so one day i might be broken.

I AM
MORE
THAN
JUST
ONE ME.

16

layered conversations

emotions are ever-flowing and changing like the rising and falling tides of the sea, yet our phones aren't good at explaining that idea. we live in a day of interpretation. we guess at how the other person is feeling because we received (at best) a text message or (at worst) a simple emoji.

we infer.

we gamble.

we assume what the other person means but it's next to impossible to truly know unless we ask with our mouths.

that's the beauty of phone calls and conversations over coffee or drinks – face-to-face. it's of course easier to Snap and swipe and Tweet and message, but i don't think it's better.

how many times have we been wrong in assuming that someone meant something they didn't actually mean because we read it that way? we place our own feelings on their emotions and everything becomes a mess.

"your text made it seem like you were mad at me. you didn't even use an exclamation point!"

there is no real replacement for watching her talk or listening to him explain a situation. especially when it matters, and i'd argue it matters more than we'd like to admit. if you want to be in a relationship that lasts, one that means more than the moment, then pick up the phone or send an actual invitation to meet up for a worthwhile conversation.

take the time to know her heart.

take the time to understand his truth.

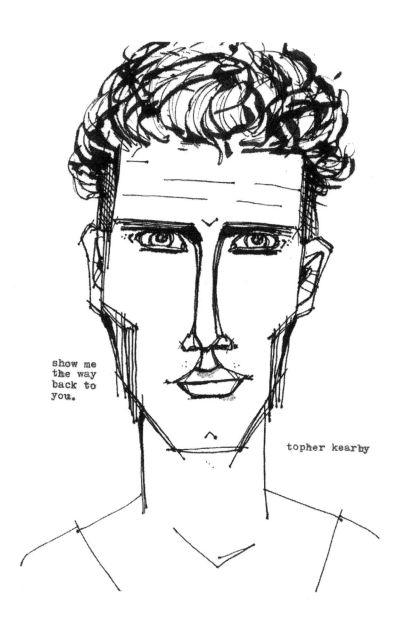

show me
the way
back to
you.

topher kearby

park

i watched her walk away from the park bench
and i could tell that the man she left behind was
heartbroken. he slumped his shoulders, his face was
covered by his hands, and i could hear him weep quietly.

she didn't look back.

we've all probably been on both sides of that
conversation – the broken and the breaker. one heart is
ready to move on and the other may never feel the same.
that's why love is so cherished and so feared. it feels
euphoric when it rests inside of you and hurts like hell
once it is removed.

often we have no choice when either happens.

i watched my children play for a while longer
in hopes that the man would gather himself enough to
move on. he never really did. i walked over to him and
softly said, "it will be okay. give it some time."

to his credit the man nodded his head in silent
agreement, and in that moment we shared a conversation
that humans have been having since the beginning of
time:

i understand you.
i appreciate your pain.
life will go on.

HE WAS
THE COOL
GUY WITH
THE CHILL
SMILE
AND HIS
SECRETS
WOULD
MAKE You
WEEP.

20

cool guy

must be easy to be the guy who wakes up and brushes
his teeth with a hammer and rinses his mouth with small
batch bourbon.

he slips on a pair of steel toed Chuck Taylors and goes to
work making leather saddles by hand while his perfectly
combed hair attracts honey bees by the bushel.

lunch break is his chance to ride his unrestored Indian
Chief motorcycle to the local café and order black coffee
and catch the eye of every eye in the place.

he speaks very little and says exactly what he wants to
say even if you don't want to hear it, but then after he
says it you'll wish it was your idea.

he's chill in the fire.

he's hot in the ice.

if he's said something once

he won't need to say it twice.

afternoons are spent gathering scrap metal for his
welding projects that are on display at the Louvre.

he sleeps in a cave and makes breakfast for kings,

that's when he isn't fitting Hollywood starlets with
custom made jewelry and rings.

he's an everyman.

he's no man at all.

and the whole damn world is just waiting to see him fall.

22

less

some days we fail.
we are less in the evening than we set out
to be in the morning;
nothing went as planned,
and everything fell to pieces.
we shake tired fists and cry worried tears,
wondering why we can't be more.
it's a lonely, painful ache to not feel good enough,
even for ourselves.
we've all had those days
and we will have so many more.
pearly white smiles of social media
paint impossible portraits of impossible lives,
and we hurt because our teeth are yellow
and we broke all our resolutions.
it's okay.
shit happens and it happens all the time.
it will be okay and we will be okay
because we know this isn't an exclusive feeling
to just you or me.
being human is just difficult some days.
you are loved.
you are enough.
tomorrow will come and it may suck again
or it might be amazing.
just don't give up.

24

shopping carts and hope

both of her hands were wrapped tightly around the handle of a bright red Target shopping cart.

three children (her children i can only assume) were circling her like lionesses on the hunt. she'd clearly been prey before and the actions of the pride didn't seem to bother her. she was in control of the situation.

one by one the children came to her with a variety of needs and wants, and one by one she answered them with patience and understanding. it was a beautiful ballet performed just a few feet away from the snack shop.

these were brief moments during a quick couple of minutes that i shared with a stranger in a superstore, but what i saw then and what i still remember now will stay with me for the rest of my life:

hope.

her eyes sparkled as she looked at her children in only the way a mother's eyes could. she saw within her tiny wild tribe a beautiful future that did not need to be tamed, and that sort of thinking is a rare gift.

one day her children will look back and be thankful for minutes like these spent with a mother like her near the snack shop of an ordinary superstore just past Main Street.

YOU SHOULD
HAVE
BROKEN MY
HEART
SOONER.

WOULD HAVE
BEEN KINDER
THAN LEADING
ME ON ALL
THIS TIME.

whiskey flowers

i found your memories all gathered up like freshly picked flowers at the bottom of another empty whiskey bottle last night.

i keep telling myself that i'll quit torturing myself with these dark midnight trips down memory lane, but like you always said, "ain't nobody who can lie to themselves better than you."

you were right back then and you still are now, as my room starts to spin up feelings that would gladly take the night off if i let them, but i don't because i can't.

i'm sick with the missing you disease, the lamenting us plague, the too much of myself cancer. any one of those has been known to kill sad men like me and it seems i have them all at once.

one last tip of the glass and the world turns black and my broken heart finally shuts the hell up for a moment. it's not healthy but like i said i'm already sick, so i might as well meet my maker with an empty bottle in my right hand. heaven seems like the kind of place i might get thrown out of so i need to be ready for one last fight.

i love you, darling, and i always will,

i'll always be the wild man who never stopped fighting for you.

28

old man and the cane

the wooden cane's handle curved just under the old
man's palm, like the Saint Louis arch at sunset. it was a
beautiful image of strength and fragility – the wooden
cane strong and unyielding and the old man's hand soft
and flexible. they were partners in this end of life dance
and they had clearly been practicing their routine for a
while.

his knees shook with each step and the wooden stick
remained resilient in his hand. an infinity of concrete
pavement marked the path ahead. funny how you never
notice the cracked and broken pieces of a sidewalk until
you have to focus on each step. one wrong placement of
the cane or a foot and everything falls down.

of course he didn't miss a step.

after a couple of minutes he made his way to the door
and i stepped in front of him to help him through the
entrance. he had a plaid fedora on the top of his head. it
sat awkwardly as if it might fall off at any moment but it
never did. i smiled and said, "beautiful day out today."

he looked up at me, his back was curved nearly as much
as the handle of his cane, and he smiled a wrinkly
tightlipped smile. he winked, tapped the rubber tip of his
cane against the concrete, and spoke just a few words
that I'm sure will never leave me.

"life doesn't ask permission to have good days. they just
happen. same with bad. so no need to worry, son. you'll
get old just like me someday and don't think that's a bad
thing. life tends to sort itself out with each year further
away from youth. by the time you're bent over like me
you'll have it all figured out."

a second wink and a final nod was his goodbye to me as
he walked through the now opened hospital doors. i was

so stunned by the gravity of his words that all i could think to say was, "thank you." i'm not sure he even heard me speak but i was thankful all the same.

i forgot where i was going for a minute and just stared at the gray spring sky. what a gift that man was in my life that day.

the world is fuller. lives are brighter. because somewhere an old man with his hand on a wooden cane is speaking wisdom to an unsuspecting ear.

die old with me

die old with me,
unspectacularly.
beneath an old oak
tree
while the last summer sun
sets.

grow old and gray with me
slowly,
as calendar days glide to the floor
unceremoniously.

no pomp and circumstance,
no final words,
just two people who spent a life
loving each other,
hanging on for Earth's
final turn.

I'M
WORRIED
ALL
I'LL
EVER
FEEL
IS
LOST

33

sometimes

the bar was empty
except for me and a few scattered loners.
a plump man in his sixties wore a Cubs baseball cap
and disappointedly scratched off a tall stack
of dollar lottery tickets while he drank pints
of cheap beer and grumbled about this and that.
a teenage boy swept the linoleum floor
with a wide broom.
his face was sour like he hated everything,
and maybe he did.

i was there with my pen and paper.

she sat at the far edge of the bar swirling her watch
around her wrist as if it were a cocktail.
a pack of nearly empty cigarettes balanced perfectly
on a mint green colored lighter next to her right hand.
"it's all shit," she murmured to no one and everyone.

i heard her and nodded.
"sometimes," i replied.

she smiled in my direction,
"guess you're lost too."

"sometimes," i replied.

SUCH AN EXQUISITE

PAIN IS LOVE.

loved me like you did

you shouldn't have loved me
like you did,
but you did love me like you did,
unaware that i was unlovable, unfixable, unworthy
of a love like yours,
but you went ahead still loving me
as if all my fractured puzzle pieces somehow
made perfect sense to you.

you never offered to *fix* the broken parts,
or mend the frayed scraps of past mistakes
dangling off my back like party streamers
from a celebration of the worst kind.

you were better than me,
stronger than me,
more of you than i was of me
at any time in my entire life,
and you loved me still,
even though i spent the entire time convincing you
that you could do better,
should do better,
must do better than me.
still, you stayed.

not just stayed,
you made me your home,
and i was happy in that place with you.
i am certain i did my best to make you leave,
but you didn't go.
you never left.

i did.

because everyone is better off without me
in the end.

killers

it's the ones you'd least expect that have bodies buried
under the floorboards in their living rooms. they are
bishops at the local church and boy scout leaders with
perfect resumes. perfect lives and perfect wives with
perfect kids and white picket fences, but the smell can't
stay hidden for long.

they go to work and drive sedans with recently detailed
minivans parked in the garage. suits are pressed and
shirts are tucked in tightly behind woven leather belts as
they hand out pancakes at the town's fundraiser. the trick
is to smile so wide that your face hurts so no one notices
that your eyes are dead or full of rage.

i notice.

perfect people scare me.

the ones who show their fangs a little are the only ones
to trust. dirt under their fingernails and swear words on
their tongues, they aren't concerned with whitewashing
the dark circles under their eyes. life is hard sometimes
and they'll let you know that even if you don't ask.

i like that kind of honesty.

vices make us human and if a man doesn't have any then
he probably has too many, and that is the most
dangerous person of all.

real damages

healing happens over long stretches of time that seem to have no end, but those days do have an end and ironically enough they end with new beginnings. it's cliché to say such things but it's true. you only actually move on in life when you do indeed move on.

i remember losing my first job and it hit me like load of bricks to the chest. i couldn't breathe. i didn't eat. it was terrible. the loss stayed and stayed until i eventually decided to leave it behind and find a new start.

it wasn't easy, especially at first, but i knew life didn't care if i recovered or not. i had to find the strength within myself, and rely on the guidance of those to help me move forward. it was an intentional choice to trust in a new future, to take steps away from my past.

i still look back today all these many years later and the memory still stings a little bit. it doesn't hurt in the same way but the experience is still a part of my story. that's the thing that i think is the hardest for us to admit sometimes, that no matter how much we grow and change and climb and conquer our losses will still be a part of us in some way. that shouldn't be a negative.

the real damage happens when we stay stuck in bad situations because we are afraid to do anything else but give up or give in. we stay on the couch and eat ice cream until the pain of loss becomes our new normal.

take time to grieve loss. take time to understand mistakes. take time to reflect and grow and become more self-aware. take the time you need to heal.

just don't let life pass you by while you wait for yourself to catch back up. make the intentional choice to walk out the door and start a brand new future.

i found
myself
in the
winds of
the sea,
the storms
they made
me whole.

42

loser

much of me has been made in the fires of life.
trials have sculpted my resolve,
and hardships have built my spirit.
i've made so many mistakes that i often wake
in the middle of the night reliving the worst of them,
and nothing tells me i won't make more tomorrow.
i'm okay with that.

the easy days are a nice break, of course,
but i don't remember many.
i'm sure every sunset is different but at the end
they all just blend into a single lovely hue.

i love kisses and coffee and sex on crisp sheets.
i'm human.
i laugh more than anyone would ever guess.
life is a joy that i'm happy to live.

that being said,
i think more about hardships than victories.
failures are the fuel that keep my lights on at night,
and maybe there was a time where that bothered me.

but these days it just makes me proud to be me –
someone who is content with not winning..

gentleman, be a gentle man

open the car door, you slug, that person standing next to you is a genuine lady.

take off your suit jacket or that forty-dollar H&M hoodie and lay it down on that puddle so her shoes don't get soaked. it just rained, you idiot. use your head and quit adjusting yourself every five seconds. everything is still there but if you keep checking your junk, she will be long gone.

you're selfish. get better.

your mom gave you far too many hugs and never had you put away the dishes and now you think everything you do around the house is for her. what a treat. she's so lucky to have you.

grow the hell up.

be a damn gentleman.

one day you might have a baby together and when that day comes wake up all night and change diapers and warm bottles. you're not going the extra mile to help. you're doing your job. you're tired? quit crying.

be a man.

be a gentle man.

bring home flowers and put them in a vase and set that vase on the side of the bed where your love sleeps. ask her what her favorite flowers are and buy those flowers. do this just because you love her. expect nothing in return. your love life isn't a Merril Lynch investment portfolio, you piece of garbage.

rub her back and open your ears. and chop wood for the fireplace. fires are romantic and you should be romantic and you should put your phone down and quit checking

ESPN for college football scores at dinner. that's
disgusting and you know it.

be better than all of the other trash guys who sell their
poison as perfume on the corner of every street.

love her, man. love her completely, as if you will
literally die without her because you just might. you
don't even know how to spell v-i-t-a-m-i-n.

be calm.

be kind.

connect with her through your words and your mind.

put her first.

everything else, you put last.

hold her purse when she needs to go the restroom after a
movie. you know you secretly think you look good with
it on your shoulder. it's a good color and your eyes are a
good color. you rock that purse, mister, and she knows
you rock it too.

she's too good and sometimes that will make you feel
bad. because you want to be better and you just aren't
most days. she's amazing and you've put on the same
sweatpants for a week. toss them in the washer with a
few more loads and shut up about it. no one needs to
know you did it for it to be done.

be better, men.

be gentle, man.

be everything she already knows you can be.

i live in a world
of words and
dreams,
a world where
anything is
possible.

- topher kearby

art for you

there is a woman in a dim room,
currently writing what might just be
the most beautiful lines of prose ever inked on paper.

perhaps a few miles down the road
there is a man painting what will eventually
be labeled a masterpiece.

neither know that the other exists
and that's okay.

not every line or every brush stroke
is meant to be consumed and analyzed instantly.
the most important part of creating
is creating for yourself.

it is far too easy to lose your voice
trying to constantly speak to the crowd.

thrift store love

i place our photograph in the frame
we stole from the thrift store.
well, you actually stole it,
i went back in and paid for it,
that and the book of Emily Dickinson poetry
you kept flipping through and setting back
down on any number of random shelves in the shop.
you always did that, as if half-expecting me
to put the item back in its right place.
i always did.

still, it's nice to remember the times
when we were at our happiest.
our best days were usually the ones we didn't
plan to do anything special,
yet those moments became priceless.

now as i look out and see the moon
that you liked to call your own,
and adjust the photo in the frame,
i resolve to plan less and just *be*
more with you.

maybe this year is the year
we remember why we fell in love.

51

when you wake

i've come to the realization that i don't
have as many days left on this planet as i'd like,
and it feels like fire in my blood.
there have been so many moments
where the number of days before me
felt like too many.
i'd done enough,
so it was all right if my future evaporated
like cool rain falling against hot asphalt,
i'd just watch my dreams turn to streams
and nod my head with contentment.

things, oh how they change,
and you wake.
not wake from a night of sleep,
your dreams so blurred by the day you can only
remember shadowed faces,
no – you *wake.*

you realize the person you still are,
and what there still is to do.
you stop being okay with letting days race by
and start to long to make the most of the days
you still have yet to live.

53

snow angels

we made snow angels in the park
next to the garbage cans full of recyclables
and looked up at the blue sky and wondered
about the stars behind the clouds.
it started to rain and some of the kids cried
but we didn't move much;
we were already wet and the icy rain
felt like heaven for a moment,
and a moment of heaven is worth soggy jeans
we probably both would have thought,
if you were there with me,
but you weren't.
maybe you were somewhere making snow angels
in a puddle of mud like i was,
maybe even thinking about me,
but probably not.
the kids at the park looked away and
held their mothers' hands so tightly
as they ran by me.

i'm the crazy one now,
without my crazy love
that made everything make more sense.

at least i got a moment of heaven that day
amidst my lifetime in the dirt.

sorry for you, poet

maybe it was the menacing glint in her eyes, or the way the young woman's pointed smile cracked her emaciated cheeks, or perhaps it was the blood-soaked machete wrapped tightly by her slender fingers that told me she was in the mood for violence.

i clicked and clacked the keys of my Corona folding portable typewriter (with case and manual) in an attempt to express my feelings about the moment:

she is love. love is an ocean. i am chaos. my heart is a wildfire. love never stops loving, lovers do. the moon broke my heart. hurricanes hurt but so do lovers.

i typed and i cried from the beauty of it all until i used up all of the square shaped bar napkins.

"what the hell are you doing?" the machete wielding woman asked. "your sobbing is distracting me from enjoying my beer. and i really want to enjoy my beer."

black leather boots hit heavy against the sticky liquor covered concrete floor as she made her way to my booth.

the lighting was terrible for reading but the dripping droplets of fresh blood raining down from her blade encouraged me to keep my mouth shut while she bent over and reviewed my work.

"so?" i spit the word out like it had been stuck in my mouth for a lifetime. "what do you think?"

a thick glob of saliva shot from her mouth and splattered against my typed pieces of prose.

"i feel sorry for your typewriter, poet," she said, her face soaked with distain. "i feel sorry that my eyes had to suffer through reading that shit."

i squealed with delight. "so you really think i'm a poet?"

WHAT I AM
BECOMING IS
SO MUCH MORE
THAN YOU COULD
EVER SEE.

all you are

the world will never understand all that you are.
no lover will ever pull every ounce of you
from your eager lips,
nor will any friend dig deep enough to uncover
the entirety of your buried identity.
no, that isn't how humanity works.
being a human is meant to be a personal experience,
a journey started and finished by one.

screaming into the world we are born,
and tired our bones are eventually placed in the ground.
that's a beautiful life,
to begin and to end, no matter what fills in the gaps,
and you will be the only person to truly understand
your story completely,
the only one to fully appreciate the lyrics
and offbeat rhythm to your song.

so, let's stop putting so much pressure on other people
to fulfill our personal needs.
that's our job and it's why being in any form of
relationship is so damn difficult.
most of us haven't taken the time to know ourselves,
to understand our needs,
to unwrap the wonderful layers of our souls.

take selfish moments to love yourself.
say no to the crowds and screens that demand
your attention and adoration.

it's all worth nothing if you don't take the time
to know the worth of your self.

familiar stranger

shadowed stranger at my door,
you knock when no one is looking,
you enter my home without invitation,
and you take everything you desire
without permission.

you sit and you eat every good thing
that i have gathered.
you spit and you curse and you mess.
you wake when the house is meant to be sleeping.
you slumber without needing rest.

you are a restless reminder of everything
that i am not.
you are an ache in my belly –
my unrealized hopes.

anxiety,

you ghost that never shows your face,
you godlike cloud of smoke and dread,
you know everything,
and see everything,
want everything,
and consume everything.

you are as real as the air i breathe
even though i cannot touch you.

go away and be lost with the other ancient spirits,
bury yourself deep down in the dirt,
for my life is meant for something
more than you can offer,
my heart is ready for happiness,
and tired of all your hurt.

WHAT HAVE I BECOME?

science fiction

these heavens and these moons,
these stars and these dripping droplets of sunlight
from orange autumn sunsets,
these trees and these emerald shaking leaves,
these tire marks black with rubber tar,
how far we've come.
gasoline stations pumping dinosaur blood,
factories and rollerblade competitions on television,
microwaved diet plans
and delivery robots who know how to smile.

these years and these long-stretched Saturday nights,
these eyes and these steady breaths
from trembling wanting lips,
these sugars and these varieties of imported spices,
these fingers with knuckles and bones,
look at how far we've come.
high schools with skate park ramps in the classroom,
axes and chainsaws that cut through metal piping,
time-traveling greeters and the superstores
and milkmen who never miss a house.

these fires in my mind and these storms,
these car crashes and these abandoned foreclosed homes,
from jumbled happy moments
these lonely hearts with shotgun holes,

these light bulbs that never burn out,
oh my, look at how far we've come.

lovers and poets that somehow write and live,
rain and slip-and-slides just outside the windowsill,
broccoli cheddar breakfast cereal
and tap dancing reality tv police stars
who never miss a shot,
look at how far we've come.

what an amazing fantasy life.

grotesque

if i asked you to pull the muscles
and skin from my bones,
to crack my ribs open so you could
see my beating heart,
i am certain you'd refuse.

such a request is grotesque,
inhumane,
and would make any normal human
recoil, or worse.

yet here i stand
asking you to love me,
and i feel like it's the same request.

napkin manifesto

the way she looked at me, i could tell she had something
on her mind. the gears inside her skull were cranking
over and over again like the guts of Big Ben. i could
almost hear the metal clanging against metal.

thinker.

she didn't speak to me then and i haven't seen her since
but there was a long few minutes were she just stared in
my direction. i assume it was me she was examining.
wondering, as i often do about complete strangers, why i
was there and what i was wondering.

curious.

long colorful beads roped her neck as if she were a
fortune teller on Bourbon Street. her reddish-brown hair
was untidy but her fingernails sparkled like jewels. she
wore a hoodie and a scarf even though it was ninety
degrees outside. there was something about the way she
kept looking at me that gave me pause, but i didn't look
away.

interested.

she bent her head down and fervently scribbled
something on a napkin with a pen one of the waiters left
on the table. it was an intense action. not just a signature
or a number left for the bus boy, it was a message that
she wanted to share. a passionate plea that needed to be
read. i could tell. i've scrawled those same kinds of
notes.

her manifesto.

i sipped my coffee because it was morning and i always
have coffee in the morning and i ordered two eggs with
buttered toast. i looked around the rest of the café in an
attempt to break the strange energy in the room. i noticed

windows that needed cleaning, a middle-aged couple holding hands across their table, and a single set of deep brown eyes that pulled me back to the place i was trying to escape.

connection.

she wanted me to look and see something inside of her that needed to be shared. it wasn't that i was special, or that i was in tune with the universe or that i was meant to be there in that moment, i was simply in a certain place at a certain time. i was pulled in.

hypnotized.

it is difficult to explain what happened next because it sounds like magic or some sort of alien abduction story, but the best way i can describe it was that i was put in a trance. her eyes shook with invisible energy and i'd be lying if i said that mine didn't do the same. i saw pain, hurt, hope, and love woven out before me like an undone rainbow-colored afghan. it was beautiful. it was raw.

it was real.

there is no way to know exactly how long the encounter lasted, maybe no more than a second but perhaps as long as a few minutes. i don't remember, but i do recall almost breaking the ceramic coffee mug in my hand once it was done. i hadn't realized how hard i was holding on until a waitress asked me if i was all right.

"i think so."

the woman with the beaded necklaces and perfectly painted fingernails laid the napkin on my table when she left the diner. she didn't say a word. i unfolded the white paper and read aloud what she had written.

"open your eyes. you're missing everything."

so i did.

i ramble when i'm scared

have you ever been frightened to your core by a passerby on the street?

of course you have.

humans are scary beasts.

i don't mean that rough looking fella with a teardrop tattoo etched on the tip of his cheek as if it were menace personified. i mean a Mr. Smith type of guy or a Sally Sue kind of girl that makes you shiver unexpectedly.

he probably has bodies in his basement.

she definitely has something to hide.

i wonder about people like that sometimes, and usually my mind goes to that place when someone is too buttoned up – starched collars and polo horses sewn on the elastic bands of their underwear. too good usually means you are very bad.

the quiet guy next door is usually to blame.

but i'm sure people feel the same about me. no normal person dresses in all black during the middle of summer. plus i often have to remind my lips to smile. and i talk aloud to myself more often than is socially acceptable.

who do we really know anyway?

especially nowadays where we carry the world's population in our pockets. anyone can be anyone and that's usually the case. trust takes a lot of extra effort and additional research in the age of twenty-four hour screens and five-minute hookups.

maybe that's better.

maybe that's worse.

either way it's not how it's always been.

once upon a time in the wild wild west a man would be considered dangerous because his face was printed on a paper sign that was nailed to every shop in town. when that face rolled into Dodge people knew to be afraid.

"that's Pistol Rick. i recognize his scar."

these days anyone can be Pistol Rick with the right Snapchat filter.

don't get me wrong,

most people are good,

i believe that sort of thing, but every now and again when the right person brushes against me while i'm walking down the sidewalk my evolutionary instincts freak the hell out and i feel icy cold as if Death himself just passed me by.

and that's the scariest part.

maybe he did.

poet

i wish i were a poet,
one of those great writers dripping
smooth manicured prose from the tips
of gnawed off fingernails
onto the keys of dusty typewriters,
giving dry letters life with each saturated touch.

perhaps then i'd have the words
to tell you how true my love is,
how endless my hope is,
and how beautiful the future is
that i now see with you.

but, alas, i am no poet.
i'm just a broken man with a wounded heart,
trying my best to tell you that
i love you and i always will.

ale and secrets

the beer poured from the spout and filled up a short plump glass. the foam leveled off at the top like fog on a lake. it was a bitter hoppy ale and i drank it down as i talked with the bartender. i'm curious so i always ask too many questions. i wondered what it was like talking to curious people like myself all of the time. so i asked.

"do you like talking with people here at this bar? or would you rather people just didn't say anything?"

he laughed and rubbed his chin for a minute. he didn't have a beard but his hand seemed to trace the area of his face where a beard once was. a phantom beard that still lingered. he poured another drink for someone else then turned back to me and put his elbow on the wooden bar top.

"i like talking with people. i always have. but sometimes i hear things i wish i hadn't. people let their guard down in a place like this and i worry sometimes they regret the things they say to me, and that kind of makes me feel like i'm a thief."

"a thief?" i asked. "but they give away their stories. you're just being kind."

he sniffed in the way a man sniffs when he is thinking. just doing something other than talking, breaking the silence with a sound. "you're right," he finally said. i guess mostly i just care about people and sometimes it's hard to know that the best thing i can do for them is pour another beer or lend my ear for a minute or two. i wish i could do more, but everyone is here and gone and i am left with all their secrets."

i never expected winter
to last this long,
yet still i need to
wrap myself with heavy
wool to keep all the
warmth i have left.

MAYBE THE
WORLD IS JUST
COLD.

woven winter solitude

scarves come out when the winds change and the cold hits like a hammer to the shin.

people wrap themselves up with cotton and woven threads. wool hats and puffy jackets, sailor coats and leather boots.

we are comfortable this way because we are contained.

the world is out there and it is harsh but we are safe and warm underneath our layers of cloth and tanned hide.

conversations are fewer because it is hard to speak.

connections are limited for it is difficult to touch.

the world becomes distant and we become closer with ourselves. then suddenly, predictably, we become lost within our own minds.

we are swallowed by the gray.

too much time in our own heads isn't the best thing for most of us. it isn't the best thing for me, and that is what winter brings – forced solitude.

we are alone more.

we feel isolated more often.

the roads are slick and driving becomes treacherous and sometimes we are literally trapped.

our minds and bodies slip out of our control for a while until the warm spring rains wash away the thick winter snow and we can once again connect with the world,

and we can once again not feel so alone.

that's not
real poetry,
and i know
real poetry.
you see, i
have a degree
in my bio, so
you know i'm
an expert.
- dick

foxes

we each drip self-righteousness
from our fangs like foxes who've recently
raided the farmer's hen house.
teeth stained crimson with blood that is not
our own,
mercilessly we devour those we think
are less,
are weak,
are not as good as we are,
at least not as strong.

so we come again and again with clean consciences
in the dark with our
pearly whites sparkling under the moonlit sky
to prove we are better than someone else
for a moment.

to prove we are powerful
for an instant.

we are beasts
who ache to feed on the tender meats
pulled from someone else's self-doubt.

once

heaven sat on my shoulder one humid summer afternoon
and whispered sweet secrets of the universe in my ear.
i'd love to repeat each word to you,
but sadly i cannot remember what was spoken.
it was a moment meant to live and die
in
the
moment.

to be beautifully forgotten,
to be wonderfully lost,
to be given back to the heavens
from which it was taken.

not every wonderful experience can be recorded,
not all life is meant for film and prose;
it is plenty good enough
just
to
live everything once.

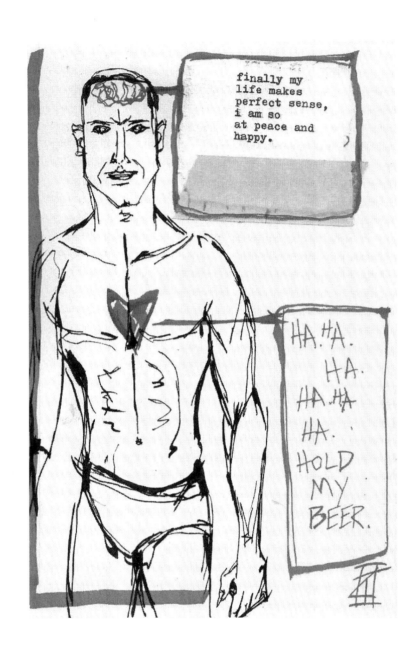

all in

if you are going to love then why not go all in?

take every risk,
drive every damn mile,
spend every dime you can dig up from your
stained couch cushions.

make a fool of yourself.
put your foot in your mouth.

say i love you way too many times
and risk looking like an absolute fool in public.
who gives a shit what other people think?

this could be the most amazing time
in your whole damn life.

don't you dare waste it.

crazy heart

gas in my jeep
and seemingly infinite highway ahead.
windshield sparkling with mental sunshine
even though it's been raining for days
or hours
or to be honest i can't remember
because all i want to do is drive,
escape,
be alone with my thoughts
and my crazy heart that won't let me
give up on impossible dreams
even though life has told me
many times to quit.

i need to think,
i need to center myself
and drink inspiration from a new well
outside my normal path.
to be reborn,
again and again
and perhaps again if needed.

i'm not turning back
and that's enough of a map
to get me where i'm going.

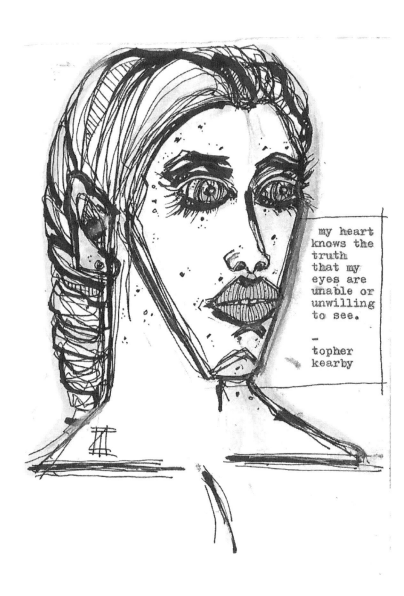

my heart
knows the
truth
that my
eyes are
unable or
unwilling
to see.

-
topher
kearby

broken words

she watched the man yell as if she was viewing a rerun on television. she'd seen this all before and seemed unfazed by the brute's persistent insults, and he *was* persistent.

the man's lips moved violently and his fists raised and lowered next to his body like hammers on the end of rubber bands. at any moment he could have snapped and struck her, but thankfully he didn't. not this time at least.

the woman didn't look scared. she looked vacant – empty. the person she once was left a while ago i assumed. nodding in agreement with the man's angry tirade she softly spoke, "i know. you're right. you're always right. i'm sorry."

the man went on yelling. he hadn't heard her speak. how could he have? his internal radio was locked solely on his own voice, and he clearly loved the frequency.

the woman dropped her head in defeat and for the first time her face flooded with real emotion. she began to weep as if the concrete mask she worked so hard to keep steady on her face finally became too heavy to bear.

"oh, and now i have to put up with the shit," the angry man spat. "you're crying now? here? typical!"

"dear, do you need me to call you a ride? or the police?" a kind elderly lady asked. she spoke calmly but with an undeniable authority.

the woman smiled slightly and wiped the tears from her eyes. "thank you, but i'm okay." she straightened her back and shot a stare so bright and clear that i swear i could smell the angry man's skin begin to smolder. "i've taken too much for too long. i'm leaving with the car and i won't be coming back."

without another word, she stepped off of the sidewalk and opened the driver side door of her gray Ford Taurus. in the span of no more than a few seconds she drove off down the road and disappeared into the night.

the man shook his head in disbelief and patted his pockets like he was searching for something. "my phone! my phone was in that car!" he looked around frantically. "does anyone have one i can borrow?"

"i need to save my battery for a call that matters," the elderly woman said. "besides there's no one left who's willing to hear what you have to say."

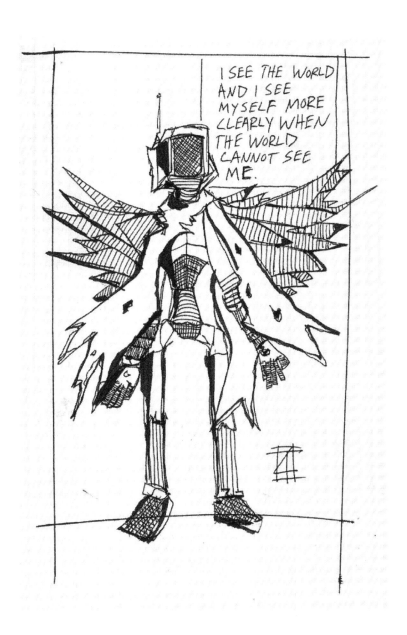

I SEE THE WORLD
AND I SEE
MYSELF MORE
CLEARLY WHEN
THE WORLD
CANNOT SEE
ME.

world's view

to be lost in the blowing winds of a prairie somewhere
far off of the worn roadways of life. to find myself
amongst the dense trees of a sprawling forest that
seemingly has no end. to dive deep into the crystal blue
ocean and be able to fill my eyes with the rainbow
colored wildlife all around me.

to be alone,

to have time to think,

to dig into the dirt that covers the graveyard of my mind,

to take the luxuriously selfish time to understand what i
actually want and need to be happy.

there are too many stoplights now. there are too many
paved roads. there are too many strip malls and
underwear specialty stores. we've become prisoners to
need. each of us just as free as any prisoner locked up for
crimes against society. bright lights cover billboards and
yet few of us shine any honest lights on our souls. what
are we afraid of finding?

"who am i?"
"who cares," they say. "just keep in line."

it's a bit of jealousy that one encounters when you take
time to think and wonder. dreamers don't add much to
the standard way of thinking. we, those who are often
lost in thought, are viewed as wasteful of our days. yet,
nothing could be more valuable than slowing down.

"what is the meaning of life?"

"who knows," they say. "just spend your money."

collections and closets filled to the brim with plastic and scraps of cloth and yet our hearts are as empty as our bank accounts. we are broke. we are shattered. we are not made to live without time to think and ponder our existence. dreaming is the essential act that makes us human and yet we sacrifice dreams to live in ways that make sense to everyone else.

"why am i here?"

"you know, i've always wondered that too," they say.

"you have?"

"of course. when i was younger i thought about it."

"and now?"

"i'm too tired, too busy to care."

life doesn't make it easy, i understand. it takes as much effort to plan time to think as it does to make time to study, work, play, watch, travel, parent, build a relationship, etc. everything takes effort. we all have the same amount of hours. why not use a few of them to get to know yourself better?

"want to hang out tonight?"

"sorry," they now say. "taking time tonight for me."

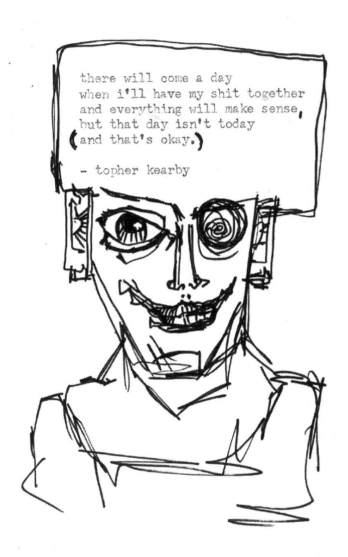

there will come a day
when i'll have my shit together
and everything will make sense,
but that day isn't today
(and that's okay.)

- topher kearby

manic

scrambled eggs on the brain
and the bacon isn't even fried yet.

mornings come and go but my thoughts
left on the last train to tomorrow land
before i even opened my eyes
or made my first mistake.

click clack.
let's leave the now and spend
every waking second in a future that may
never be realized
except in the fantasies
of a deranged maniac who looks
an awful lot like me in the fogged
mirror that hangs crooked
above my toilet.

i'm a sham.
i'm a shadow.
i'm little more than a character
on a stage with no audience
except the voices inside my head
and they are too loud to sort
out if i'm remembering my lines
or if i've completely gone off script.

the pursuit of a life well lived

our culture places too much
value on careers
and not enough value
on personal happiness.

if someone takes a job that isn't necessarily personally
fulfilling in order to pay enough bills so he can spend
more time truly living, that person is viewed as weird or
maybe even lazy. yet, when you focus your energy on
the pursuit of true happiness instead of advancing in the
traditional workplace you begin to discover that real joy
is found through experiences and not the amount of
money in your portfolio.

of course my opinion is little more than typed words on
paper – meaningless. these are the ideas and ramblings
of a confessed weirdo, but i am personally at a point in
my life where i understand why i've never found a true
career for myself – i don't value that lifestyle.

my passion is living simply and loving fully.

i want those ideals to be a catalyst for a life well lived.

conversations on the plane

a man sat silently next to me on a flight to Salt Lake City. he was young in the face but old in the eyes. there was a weariness that colored his pale skin. his phone was gripped tightly in his hand as if it might run off at any moment and never return. he rocked uneasily in his seat. not too much to make me worry but just enough to make me wonder.

i keep to myself typically. it's just easier than making conversation. other people have the gift of casual chat but i wasn't given that trait. still, something about him made me ask, "you okay, man?"

he shook his head unconvincingly. "yeah, i'm good."

"my name is Topher. just ask if you need anything or whatever." i added the 'whatever' to the end of my statement as proof of my social awkwardness. "you flying to Salt Lake?"

"yeah. meeting my girlfriend. i mean…" he trailed off a bit. "i was supposed to be meeting her, but i guess not now."

it was at this moment i realized i'd bitten off more than i expected. normally people just say "i'm fine" and go on with their lives. not this man. not this time. he needed to get something off his mind.

"sorry to hear it didn't work out." i said this not knowing what else to say. "what happened?" *shit. why did i ask that? why didn't i just leave it alone. now i'm invested.*

"i don't know. she just messaged me not to come, but it's too late."

i kept quiet for a moment or two. not because i was trying to end the conversation, i just didn't know what to say. i nodded and finally said, "sorry" again.

he shook his moppy brown hair as if he were a cow shaking a fly from its nose as he scrolled through pages of pictures on his phone. i caught a glimpse of a dark-haired thin-faced girl holding his hand on a touristy beach somewhere probably in Florida, and another of him and the same girl riding a hay wagon. they seemed happy but who doesn't in pictures?

the flight went on for a few hours and i fidgeted in my seat the entire time. i try to relax on planes but it's difficult to feel comfortable. finally the plane landed and everyone was grabbing their bags from the overhead storage bins and rushing off the plane. i leaned over to my broken-hearted flying companion and said, "you'll be all right, man. i promise."

i thought to myself that it was stupid to promise this stranger anything because i had no sort of power over time and space, but i regularly say stupid things so i just brushed it off and grabbed my backpack.

"i hope so," he said.

i stepped back and watched him grab his suitcase and walk solemnly down the aisle. it was incredibly heartbreaking because i knew just what he was feeling.

we both stepped into the airport and i think i remember my jaw breaking off from my face and falling to the floor. the dark-haired girl with the thin face was standing there waiting. she held in one hand about half a dozen red roses and in the other hand she covered her eyes. she seemed to be crying. the sad guy from the plane didn't hesitate. he walked right over to her and wrapped his thick arms around her shoulders.

i smiled but it quickly faded as i kept walking. i was happy it worked out for him, but it doesn't always end like that for the rest of us.

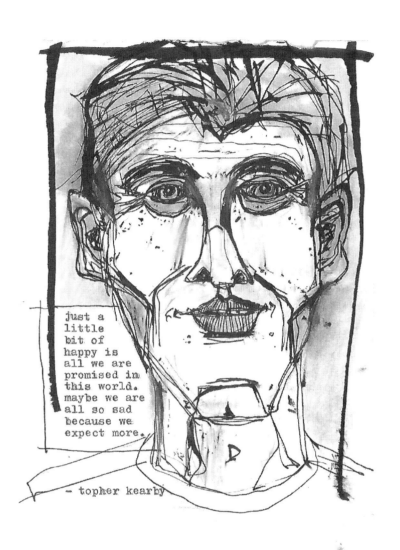

just a
little
bit of
happy is
all we are
promised in
this world.
maybe we are
all so sad
because we
expect more.

— topher kearby

101

simple happiness

the world will tell you that a little isn't much of
anything. the world is wrong. a little is more than a lot.
that sounds like a riddle and maybe it is but if you are
brave enough to decide that less is indeed more you'll
see yourself becoming a more fulfilled human.

not everything is important.

i've spent most of my adult life spreading myself thin
like hot butter on burnt toast. i was everywhere and
nowhere in particular. it's a symptom of our time.
everyone can reach anyone any time of day and no one
has any time to focus on what is actually important. we
are now an ocean of people attempting to do everything
pretty well and have lost the idea of discovering a true
calling. most of us at least.

joy is the priority.

what will make you content? it's such a sugary selfish
question. personal happiness is often viewed in the same
light as a sexually transmitted disease. "gross. he is so
happy. what the hell is wrong with him?" tell someone
you are making yourself a priority and they will burn
you in effigy once you turn and walk the other way.
that's okay. just use the flames to keep you warm. let go
of what others think of you as much as you possibly can.
in truth, most people don't think about you as much as
you think about them thinking about you. you are here
and gone and they move on to the next person to roll
their eyes at.

too much is too much.

if you dug down deep into your guts and pulled out what was really important to you i wonder what you'd find. would it be to be rich? to be famous? to be seen as successful to your peers and family? or just maybe it would be something else altogether? something beautiful? something real? something that has nothing to do with how others see you and everything to do with the proper calling of your heart?

"take your own medicine, Topher. what's deep down in your guts?"

i want to be loved, to show love, to write, and to make art. preferably lost somewhere in the countryside out of the way of all these sidewalks and traffic lights that feel more and more like cages than guides. i want to wake up and take a long walk down a gravel road for no other reason than it was a perfect morning. i want to watch my girls grow up happy and hold their hands as they decide to pursue whatever their hearts have called them to do. i want to have deep talks with my friends and breathe in the pure air at the top of the Rocky Mountains. i want to be stupid happy and cut out the rest.

life is too short.

THE END DIDN'T COME WITH FIRE, IT CAME WITH TIME.

end of ourselves

little by little we chisel off pieces of ourselves to fit into our relationships. lovers – at first – love everything about each other. simple things that make us smile at first end up being the things that eventually drive us mad. so we go to work with words and strategies to make each other more compatible.

it's not so painful while you're living it but once you are away and look back you realize how much of yourself was lost for that time. that's when the pain hits. the empty feeling down at the bottom of your soul that you aren't who you want to be any longer.

lovers aren't the only ones who shape us; friends often wield the heaviest of mallets and sharpest of saw blades. we start when we are very young, sculpting the people around us to make our lives more comfortable, or we start allowing others to mold us to make their lives easier.

everyone ends up looking about the same when it's all said and done. everyone ends up thinking alike. everyone fits in with everyone else pretty much. it's simpler that way. yet, no one is really happy in the end because no one is anyone anymore.

slowly, bit by bit, piece by piece, we give ourselves away to everyone else thinking that it will be better that way. we think it will be easier that way. it isn't better. it is not one bit easier. we all end up as shadows cast against blank walls, the light shining behind us but we no longer know where it comes from. the heat is on our necks but we have forgotten to look back.

it is not hopeless.

there is an art to prioritizing *yourself*. there is an art to
feeding your inner beast. there is an art to telling the
opinions of the world to get lost. there is an art to
listening to your own heart and following where it leads.
there is an art to editing out distractions. there is an art to
living. there is an art to loving fully. there is an art to
turning from the shadows and facing the sun once again.

there is an art to boldly being you.

"TO SURVIVE THIS WORLD, SOME MUST BECOME VILLAINS."

TOPHER KEARBY

107

villains and kings

that's the lie they tell us,
the villains of the world,
that to make anything you must break
a few eggs or bones.
in the end it doesn't matter what you do
to get anywhere you want to go
as long as you get there
and get there you must
otherwise you're nothing more than
a failure,
a snowflake,
a softhearted loser.
that's what they say,
those people who are on the top
looking down from their penthouse suites
at all those down below who have barely enough
if even that much.

"i've earned everything i have."
"no one has given me a damn thing."

i am sure that is true
but maybe what should truly define success
is not how much one keeps or collects
but how much one gives without expecting
anything back.

lucky ones

the lucky ones are those who feel too much,
too often, for no good reason.
they are how we all once began –
birthed, screaming into a world that was so bright
we couldn't even open our eyes to see it.

we felt everything, and we needed everything
all at once, just to survive.

it was a beautiful pain.

now, most are slaves to endless checklists and tasks,
completed over and over again until feeling *anything*
feels as though there is something wrong with us –
broken.

no.

i say, hell no, we are not broken.

we are finally fixed.

i love you
for exactly
who you are,
and i want
you to feel
free with me.

painfully inadequate

to feel love,
physically feel it warm next to your body,
pulsing with an invisible energy,
and a palpable certainty
that cannot be explained with words –
only felt in the moment
like a hand pressed firmly against a lit stovetop.

love is energy,
it moves and flows like raging rapids
reshaping flat lands into echoing canyons,
pushing through granite mountainsides,
fighting anything in its way to reach the one place
it knows it belongs.

that's why saying
"i love you"
feels so painfully inadequate at times.

if only there was
a way to filter my
heart, perhaps you
wouldn't notice how
badly it's broken.

- topher kearby

113

two artists and a lawyer

i was sipping coffee and typing on my computer at a local this-and-that shop close to my home. a man and a woman sat next to me. they wore winter jackets and drank from steaming paper cups and openly chatted about the passing walkers and cars.

they were gentle with each other. his hand rested on top of hers and she laughed easily and genuinely at his jokes. the man, probably in his mid-fifties, wore plain white running shoes and the woman, probably about the same age as him, had a plum-colored scarf wrapped around her neck. together they worked on a crossword puzzle on the back of a newspaper and shared a chocolate chip cookie she brought in her purse.

"what are you writing?" the man asked me. "you're not writing about us are you?"

his question startled me a bit and i let out a shallow uncomfortable laugh. "sorry i was probably looking your way. i just noticed how happy you two are together. i get lost in my thoughts sometimes."

the woman smiled and tapped her partner's hand. "don't mind him," she said looking up at the man, "he's always telling me stories of the people passing by. we like people watching too. we enjoy being lost in thought."

"are you a writer?" the man asked. he sipped his hot drink and gestured to my laptop.

"kind of," i replied. "i tell stories."

the woman walked over and looked at my screen. i slid to the side so she could get a better look. "oh, you're an artist too? that looks like an interesting book. all of those faces just jump right out at you."

"thank you but i'm not really an artist," i admitted.

114

"typical artist thing to say," the man said, and that brought a laugh out of both of them. "every artist i've ever known will never admit they are much of an artist, and every lawyer i've ever met can't wait to tell you how good of a lawyer they are." again they both laughed together and this time i joined in.

"he's a lawyer," she said to me with a wink.

"and she's an artist," he said, his face stretched tight with a full bright smile. "she's also the love of my life."

i watched as she fell into him like someone falls into bed after a long day's work. his arms wrapped around her tightly and he kissed her forehead and then her lips. they no longer noticed me or cared who else was in the shop, all that mattered was how much they loved each other. it was a truly beautiful moment.

sometime later i did ask if i could include them in my book. "feel free to say no," i said.

"of course," he said. "if i could shout how much she means to me from the top of every building in this city i would. i guess your book will be the next best thing."

the woman handed me a piece of paper with a phone number and an address. "please send us a copy once you're done. i just know what you're making is going to be really special."

"i promise i will," i said. "thank you."

the man stood and stretched out his hand towards me. i took hold of it and gave it a good firm shake. "never let your head override your heart," he said.

i nodded and thanked them both one last time. i walked home that night with a full heart and a spinning mind. it's amazing how the smallest moments in life can speak the loudest, how a chance meeting with two strangers can really alter your world view.

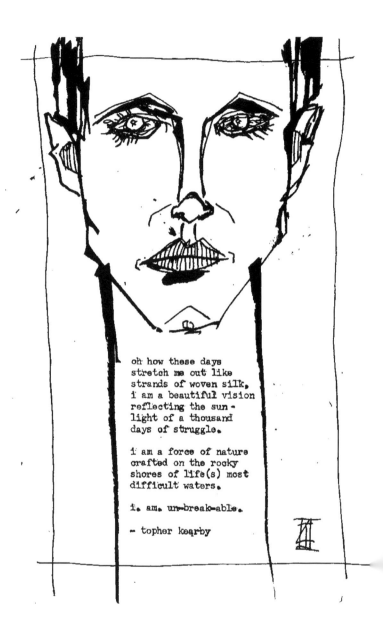

oh how these days
stretch me out like
strands of woven silk.
i am a beautiful vision
reflecting the sun -
light of a thousand
days of struggle.

i am a force of nature
crafted on the rocky
shores of life(s) most
difficult waters.

i. am. un-break-able.

- topher kearby

116

giant slayer

i wake most mornings ready
to fight the giant.
the shadowed behemoth with the easy name –
anxiety.

he's always there and never sleeps,
clearly plotting new ways
to make my stomach sick.
he's a powerful beast,
omniscient and relentless,
seemingly content to spend his time
making me nervous and unsettled.

but i breathe,
and he shakes.
i stop moving,
and he sweats.
i take time to meditate,
and he shivers.
i say the words, "i am enough,"
and he crumbles.

for i am a giant slayer,
and i have no room for his shadow
in my life.

DISAGREEABLE
PEOPLE
CHANGE
THE WORLD

TOPHER KEARBY

old man and his yard

we have become a society
of endless conversations
yet we have forgotten how to speak.
true heartfelt discussions have been replaced
with buckets of filtered phrases.
we are drowning in oceans
of saltwater words yet never actually
saying a damn thing.
we waste our moments once spent
thinking and wondering
scrolling through apps
that are meant to connect us with everyone.
it's too much.
we run out of words and forget
how to use our tongues
to form new ideas.
i know,
i am the old man yelling at the kids
to stay off his lawn,
worrying about nothing important.
fair enough.
my fear is that we all exchange so many words
so frequently
that when we really need to speak up
or speak out,
we will have nothing left to say.

it's cute
how you
 think that
 you know
 me so
 well...

love me. know me.

know me like you know yourself,
breathe in my soul and let it linger on your lips like the
countless drops of water swimming in the ancient seas.

understand the beating of my heart,
listen carefully to each and every murmur and thud as if
you were deciphering an ancient unknown language.

study the crooked wrinkles of my face,
follow each and every line with the tip of your finger
until you appreciate the life i have lived.

look into my eyes,
fall helplessly into the infinite abyss that sits just beyond
what anyone else has ever seen before.

love me,
not with some sort of hallmark romance that can be
bought and sold like plastic roses from the dollar store,
but love me so deeply that the thought of not loving me
feels like an end worse than death, for that is how i love
you, and those are the ways that i know you.

i only ask that you love and know me as i do you.

AND
HERE I
AM
STILL
LOVING
YOU.

122

empty lawn chair

you loved me when the sun was hot
and money was ripe, hanging from the vines out back,
and life was easy then and i was kind.
you smiled more and i didn't dream of driving my car
into a tree every time i drove to work.
that job will be the death of me.

delivery pizza and cheap whiskey.
i fall asleep on the green plastic lawn chair
in the guest room where your mother used to sleep
before she died last year.
we sold the bed for twenty-five dollars.

you miss your mom and i'm selfish because i miss the
days you didn't,
and you cry and i yell at the walls because i can't
stand to look at you like this.
broken people are lipstick and Christmas cards in the
movies,
but right now broken is just pain.

my heart aches more each day because i know i am
losing you.
i break my hand trying not to cry.
you'll hang a picture frame over the hole in the wall
if you come back.

i can't stop this.
i can't fix you and it makes me want to even more,
so i screw up again and once more to make it stick.

it's hard to love like this, to love so much for so long
and then to not have that love every day,
but you've gone to wherever you needed to go,
and here i am still loving you.

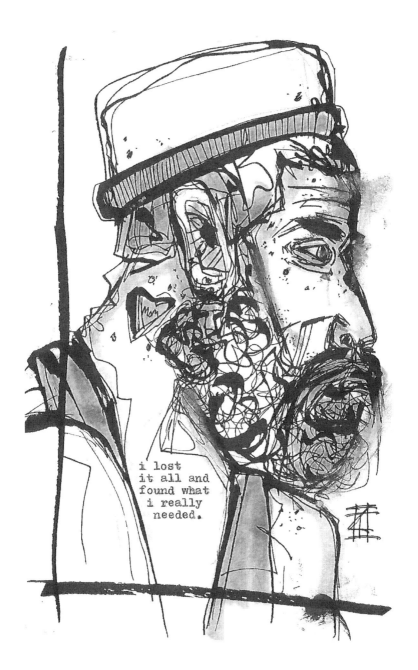

125

a dog named Phil Collins

i spent a night sleeping in my jeep at a rest stop somewhere on my way out west. it wasn't the best night of sleep i've had in my life but i didn't really need much sleep that night. life was falling apart around me and i was doing well not falling apart myself.

it was sometime past midnight when i pulled in and lines of semi-trucks were parked together like rectangular sardines in an invisible aluminum can. there weren't many cars in the parking lot, maybe just one or two besides me, so even though i was surrounded by other people i felt isolated and alone. it felt good.

i opened my door and stepped out into the night. i can't remember if it was cold or hot, i just remember seeing all of the stunning stars. you can't always see the stars when you live in the city and sometimes you might even forget they are there if you never leave the bright lights, but they never disappear.

i stretched my legs and walked around for a bit then hopped in the back of my jeep. i laid the seats down and shut my eyes and at some point a few hours later the sun came up. i was groggy but strangely happy. i needed coffee. i grabbed a couple bucks from my bag and walked towards the vending area.

i love vending machines. each one is like some sort of claw game you can always win.

there was no coffee, not sure why i thought there would be, so i paid two bucks for a cold soda. i drank a little of it right there in the soft light of the iridescent machine from which it came.

before long i was joined by a seedy looking man and his dog. we exchanged good mornings and i bent down to pet his pup. "what's her name?" i asked.

"she's a he and his name is Phil Collins," he said with not a bit of irony in his voice. "he likes to sing."

"i'm familiar with his work," i joked and he didn't laugh. i studied the man for a second or two before i stood back up. he had an untamed brown bushy beard, yellowed teeth, and his clothes looked as if they hadn't been washed in weeks. Phil Collins however looked tidy, almost like he'd been bathed recently, and well fed. "been on the road long?" i asked.

"yes," he said, "i prefer the road to anywhere else. i can always go where i want to go and no one tells me i have to stay. better that way."

"i get that," i said. "which way are you going today?"

"east," he said. "Phil Collins loves Boston this time of year." he walked over to a concrete bench and pulled out what looked like a clear container filled with dry dog food from his backpack. Phil Collins licked his lips as the man put the bowl down on the ground.

"you have everything you need on your back?" i asked.

the man bit down on a hunk of beef jerky he pulled from his jacket and spoke while he chewed. "i used to have too much and i was miserable and mean. now i have just enough and i'm happy but probably still a little mean."

"that's perfect," i said. "i'd give you a lift but i'm not heading in your direction."

"i appreciate it but we already have a ride to where we are going. just emptying our bladders and filling our guts."

i rubbed the pup's head one last time and wished them both good luck on their travels.

so many people want to be movie stars and billionaires but i still find myself envying that unkempt man and his famous singing dog.

SIGHT AND SOUND

see

what we can see with our eyes
is only half of the real story.
so much of life is lived between our ears,
inside the gray matter that spins and twists
together to form our minds.

the same event is viewed by two different
people the exact same way,
it looks the same because it is the same,
yet it feels completely different to each viewer.
we place ourselves inside each situation,
we weave ourselves into everything
even when we were never invited.

"well, if that happened to me i wouldn't have responded
like that. i would have handled things differently."

"i just don't understand how he could do that to her. i
never would have done that."

"must be easy to be her. she has no idea what real
struggle looks like. at least not like i do."

our personal way of thinking colors the landscape of our
lives and if we don't recognize that fact we will spend
our lives blinded by our own biases.

8 a.m.

the wind howls just outside my window like some
sort of wild angry cat,
hungry for more than mere scraps and field mice.
winter moves in with the frosted morning sunrise,
covering blades of short trimmed grass
with wet white powder – the kind that isn't sweet
to taste.

dim lights shine an amber shade of morning on the
smoke-colored wooden floors that my bare feet
walk across gently, as if too hard a touch
might crack the strips of stained pine.

smells of sweet syrup and black tea
swirl and twist in the air like wild Kansas cyclones,
and i must admit i feel everything all at once –
a Peterbilt truck of emotion crashes into me
and i drop to my knees.

i am crippled,
and it's only 8 a.m.

junk drawer human

i fall into the junk drawer of human existence,
in a way that no one knows what to do with me,
or more accurately,
i don't know what to do with myself.

like some oddball key that you haven't used
in seven years but are sure
it still opens something important,
or a six-foot long white cable that powers a device
that was left on the beach three summers ago.

"what the hell is this thing?"
"i don't know but don't throw it out."

that's me.

the don't-throw-it-out thing that's in the drawer
filled with other human beings that don't quite
fit in the silverware organizer or mug cabinet.

and maybe it's a good way to live
and maybe it's also a drag some days
not knowing what you're meant for.

maybe you're a writer or an artist or a this or that
kind of person, and you feel more lost that found.

133

that's cool.
at least we are in the same drawer.

and maybe that's the purpose
of not having a fixed purpose,
to team up with other misfits and weirdos,
to do amazing things that have never been done.

I WON'T LET ANYONE CHANGE ME.

135

true song

i believe there is a true song
that your heart is born singing.
the notes are pure and lovely,
and the lyrics help guide you to where
you'll eventually find your purpose.

we hear it so fiercely when we are young,
while we play, during our dreams, at the start
of each and every day, but then we age –
we make compromises that dull the tune.
days start with tired eyes from long nights
spent staring at a flashing screen.
school is reduced to black circles on white pages.
practices and responsibilities rain down
on each of us like a hurricane.

there is no time to listen,
because all our moments are filled up
with activities that are supposed to help us grow,
or at least entertain our searching minds.

life moves fast after those days of youth,
and more and more days fall like dominoes,
wasted on the pursuit of staying occupied.

eventually we forget the original song
of our heart, misplace our passions,
and dilute our purpose.

after all, such beautiful lyrics
make little sense to an organized world.
but there is still time
to find what was lost.

we just have to stop and listen.

HERE
I AM
AGAIN
STILL UNSURE
OF WHAT
TO DO.

138

why not jump?

imagine yourself standing on the top of an old bridge spanning across a wide winding river. see the distant trees and the approaching barges, notice the gentle winds brushing against your cheeks, feel the heat of the summer sun sizzling your skin.

now suck in a long steady breath. fill your lungs with new air and then let it all go. do this over and over again for a couple of long minutes. listen to the sounds of the world around you. what do you here? what is being spoken to you now that you're still?

"what do you want to say?"

"where do you want to go?"

"what do you want to do?"

i wonder what life really looks like for you when you take time to see the future with fresh eyes. i wonder where the same roads you have traveled so many times might take you when a new purpose settles into your heart. i wonder what might happen if you trust the voice inside yourself instead of following all the other voices in your life.

don't you wonder too?

140

gas station customs

holding the gas pump handle in my hand,
the smells of the $2.47 fuel hang in the air
like sweet perfume,
i watch the numbers climb and climb
with no end and i catch his eyes with my own.
i see him and he sees me,
we nod because we are two men pumping gas
at a station and that is the custom.
i look away and i can feel that he does not,
his stare sticks to my skin like a wet sweater,
so i turn to see him again.
his eyes are heavy, sunken cheeks make him look
much older than he probably is, and he has a lit cigarette
burning between two fingers.
shouldn't smoke here, i think,
but then again he's not really smoking.
he's just standing with a lit torch between his fingers.
this man looks a bit hopeless and dejected –
a balloon with no air.
i feel for him and wonder what makes his eyes heavy
and his soul seep out of his skin like the gasoline fumes
that surround us both.
then i think to myself,

i wonder if he feels the same way about me.

I THINK
I'M
HAPPY.

142

happy

"i think i'm happy," he said.

"you think? aren't you supposed to know?" she asked.

"probably. i mean, i guess i'm not sure."

that's the thing about happiness, do you ever really know what it is when you find it? i bet if you asked one hundred people on the street to define happiness you'd get nearly one hundred different replies, or at least one hundred unique ideas.

"what is happiness to you?"

"being loved."

"being a success in my mom's eyes."

"graduating at the top of my class."

"sleeping."

"creating art that lasts."

"a good man."

"music."

"delicious food."

"Christmas."

"hot coffee."

"a good book and a warm fire."

and on and on the list would go. no one ever really pinning down what true happiness looks like for everyone because there is no one-thing-for-everyone happiness pill. at least not one that lasts.

143

this freezes so many of us because there is no one path to take to make everything make sense for everyone. so we give up altogether. everyone gathers and talks about dreams over drinks and then everyone goes back home and falls asleep knowing that tomorrow a new bolder future will begin.

and then morning comes…

"great, now what do i do?"

we put on our clothes and drink our morning brews and walk out the door into the same life we had the day before. it isn't a bad life, it just isn't the one we promised ourselves we'd go after with reckless abandon. we agree to settle for a little while longer and then a little while longer once again until we end up being bones in the dirt.

to make a change you must actually be ready to make changes no matter the temporary cost, but those changes do cost and the price is high.

i'm not an expert. i'm not a self-help guide or a wise man on the top of a fog-covered mountain. i eat cold Pop-Tarts and sit on park benches while i watch sunsets. i think a lot and i write from my own experiences. those are my qualifications, but i do promise you that if you choose to make less things a priority in your life you will be happier. stop trying to figure everything out and figure out one good thing.

that is happiness to me.

burritos are a close second.

145

stouts and quiet conversations

the bartender wasn't much thicker than a blade of grass but his stories were larger than the Grand Canyon. he talked about this and that and once his shift was over he circled around to the other side of the bar top, sat down on a wooden stool, and quickly settled down as a friend.

i'm always surprised when that happens, when someone makes friends so easily. my closest friend is like that and this man was that way too. i'm different. i'm not standoffish or anything but i'd be okay sitting by myself and having a drink and just thinking.

the bartender spoke softly and told stories about how the beer was brewed and which was his favorite to have for breakfast. he drank stouts, he loved stouts, stouts were the best thing ever invented by mankind, and his favorites were imperial stouts. those were the ones he loved to have for breakfast.

if you don't know much about beer, stouts are the kind of beers you might think of when you think of Guinness, the type of brew a dwarf might drink in the Lord of the Rings movies. the kind of beer that leaves puffy remnants on one's mustache and beard, which must have been an added benefit for this man because he had a wonderfully full beard.

my friend and i sat and laughed with this man for a long while. he was so sure of who he was and what he wanted out of life. you couldn't help but admire his outlook. he admitted he was too much in some ways and not enough in others. he was honest and straightforward. he loved his job and he loved his life.

he loved stouts for breakfast.

too many of us ask for too much. life is about finding happiness where you are. wherever you are.

146

I'M OLD. NOT DEAD.

147

what we see when we look back

looking back at photographs is a difficult sort of pain.

you realize flipping through the stacks of Polaroids and Facebook posts that people who were once in your life are no longer around. death and taxes meet us in the end it's said but that doesn't sum up all the losses we must suffer through as humans.

love ends.

friendships end.

jobs and hope and joys end.

losses stack up like scrapped aluminum cans at the recycling center and eventually we run out of ways to reduce and reuse the pain.

so we keep moving.

it's easier to step forward so quickly that the hurt doesn't keep us awake at night, but when we stop it's all still there. faces of loved ones now buried deep in the ground, memories of better times when our fingers didn't throb and our children weren't too busy to call.

fuller days.

or at the very least it's how it seems when we look back.

and we always look back

even when we try our best to move forward.

149

finding self

we gather clothes and things and stuff and bags and dates and lovers and friends, yet we look at the mirror and we wonder what we are doing with our time.

lost boys and girls in a Neverland called the here and now. we are still children who were never really given a chance to grow up. isolation is treated like a sickness and the prescription is more of everything.

but the cure is less.

it costs nothing to be alone.

it costs nothing to sit and think and dream.

it costs nothing to remain still.

yet those actions create true wealth of the soul.

we eat and we cook and we buy and we write and we stretch until we are left unstrung, yet we feel empty because we've given nothing to ourselves.

it's still free to lay on your bed and look at the ceiling and wonder about your place in the universe.

it's still free to walk out of your front door and keep walking until your thoughts find you and you find them and together you are not alone.

it is still free to sit at a library and read for no other reason than reading feels good.

everyone wants to get away to find themselves yet all it really takes is finding time to look within.

I ACHE FOR SOMEONE WHO UNDERSTANDS ME.

151

everyday heroes

when you witness true strength it changes you. not
strength like a body builder, but strength like a mother
holding her sick child through the night, night after night
without a promise of an easy morning coming any time
soon. with an unfailing smile on her face and tears
spilling out of the corners of her eyes, she whispers,
"everything is going to be all right."

strength like a father desperately holding onto his
children while he speaks his familiar goodbyes. once
again he is getting deployed overseas and once again he
will miss out on his children growing up. "i'll be back
soon," he promises, "be good for your mother."

strength like a friend who's actually there for you when
no one else is. she calls you to see how you are doing. he
drives to you when you need a shoulder to cry on. she
picks you up in the middle of the night to get you out of
a bad situation. a friend who says, "whatever you need
just ask," and means it.

the list goes on and on. humans being more. people that
don't back down when life gets impossible – they stand
up. mothers and fathers and brothers and sisters and
friends and children who are willing to lift others even
when they shouldn't have to, yet still they push.

those are the ones to look up to. these everyday heroes
who understand us when we cannot be understood. the
ones who teach us that no matter what life throws in our
paths we can overcome and be more.

this world
is more than
what can
be seen.

153

young fox

i chase the sunlight through open patches in the undergrowth. this is an adolescent forest, it's numerous saplings still spry with youthfulness, gangly branches with twisted wooden fingers canopy the sapphire colored sky above me.

i pause and take notice of a young fox springing through the foliage just a few yards in front of my bare feet. i can feel the pillowy grasses beneath my toes. the fox stops for a moment and turns his head so he can look me over, as if saying, "who the hell are you?"

that's a good question, young fox, and it's perhaps the reason why i'm wandering the wilderness in the first place. "i'm no one," i speak aloud. the fox, clearly keen to understand the English language, tilts his head to the right and i swear i see him smile.

he darts back into the thickest part of the forest and is gone as quickly as a lightning strike. i scratch the scruff covering my chin and i wonder what that encounter was all about.

what did it mean?

maybe nothing.

most likely not much of something.

but just possibly it could have meant more than i'll ever truly understand.

LIFE IS
TOO SHORT
BUT TODAY
IT FEELS LIKE
IT WILL NEVER
END.

155

fighting an old man in the park

cigarette smoke puffed from his wrinkled lips
like silky smooth carcinogenic clouds.

"you're an asshole," he shouted at me.

i shrugged and kept walking. plenty of people have said worse than that to me in my life, and i didn't see the point in arguing.

"you deaf? or just stupid?" the old man was standing now. he gripped a cane with his right hand but he still looked unsteady and fragile. as if a slight wind could topple him over.

i turned and walked back to him. "you need something? want me to…"

"i need you to shut the hell up and fight me."

i have to admit i laughed. it was an honest response to one of the most awkward encounters of my life. "not going to happen," i said, keeping my distance. "i think you might be confused. are you lost?"

he spit at me and his saliva hit the pavement right in front of my feet. "coward."

the word fell off his lips with such a sensation of sadness that i felt the strange unwise urge to hug him.

so i did.

i wrapped my arms around the stranger and squeezed. his wrinkled head fell limp against my shoulder.

"it's okay," i said. "everything's all right. let me get you some help. let me call someone."

"don't need help," the old man spoke. "i'm just tired of living this life on my own. makes me angry. breaks my old damn heart. i just wanted to feel something other than weak for a minute is all. i needed to feel alive."

156

KEEP
ME
WILD?

AS IF
IT WERE
EVER
UP
TO YOU.

157

wild

she looked at me through narrow excited eyes and i
could see that she was somewhere else entirely. we were
seated around our kitchen table but perhaps she was on
Mars. my oldest daughter has an imagination unlike
most i've ever known. she has stories pinging around
inside her skull like marbles being shaken in a glass jar.

her mind is untamed.

she's been this way since birth and her younger sister is
the same. i never had to release them into the wild, to
encourage them to be wild, to tell them to be free, they
were already born free.

that's how we all came into the world.

we do dishes and make spreadsheets and vacuum floors
and go to doctor appointments. we buy lunch meat and
clip coupons and drink skim milk and go on diets to fit
into polka-dot bikinis. we occupy ourselves. we survive.

yet, give yourself an hour on a park bench without
headphones or blue screens. just sit and think and
wonder. you'll feel your soul flash hot inside your chest.
the natural you is still there waiting and you don't need
anyone to remind you of that.

you just need time to remember who the hell you are.

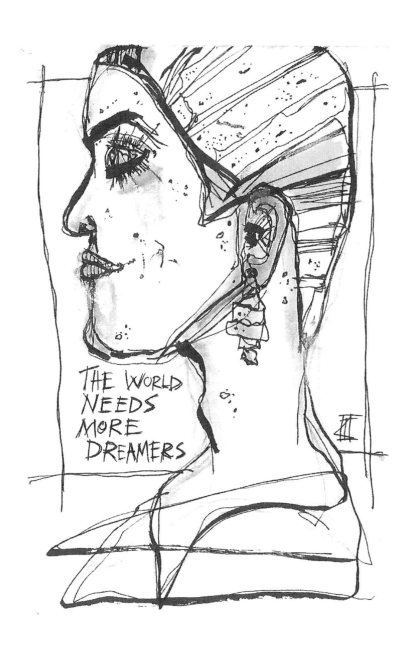

THE WORLD
NEEDS
MORE
DREAMERS

cardboard hope

she held a cardboard sign up on the corner of Main and Walnut. it said "don't give up. you're worth it."

i thought to myself that she looked a little silly holding that brown cardboard sign. the lettering seemed to have been written with a fat red sharpie and she even added a heart under the words. i did like that little bit of something. i often add hearts to the packages i send out. not sure why really, but i guess it's because i want everything i do to be about love.

of course that's what this lady was saying too, on the corner of Main and Walnut.

there was a bench of some sort or perhaps it was just a stump, i can't remember exactly but either way i sat down. a busy gas station was nearby and cars came in and out, and being the strange observer that i am i just watched for a while. she held that sign high and smiled at every car that passed.

she was genuine and not everyone liked her naturally clean smile. a fat man crammed into a square car flipped her off as he drove by. he muttered a series of harsh words, a few of which made my ears hurt. maybe he was against her message or perhaps he was just against everything.

a young mother with an Odyssey full of kids rolled down her passenger window and yelled, "god loves you!"

she ran the red light.

the woman with the sign kept smiling as i walked across the street and bought two coffees. they were gas station coffees but it was chilly and i'm pretty sure most coffee tastes the same when your body is cold. i handed her one and i kept the other. she thanked me and i smiled.

"why are you doing this?" i asked. "think it really matters in the end?"

she sipped the hot liquid from the steaming cup and thought for a second or two. the cars kept speeding by and a light rain began to fall. "it all matters," she finally said. "every ounce of everything means something to someone, and this shitty sign means something to me."

"you're my hero," i said.

and she was on that day.

that is enough in the end, i suppose, that we all find the thing that means something to us. that bit of happiness that stirs us awake at night or that slice of fear that sharpens our edge. it doesn't take much i don't think, far less than most people would realize, to make a positive impact on our world.

a scrap of cardboard and a fat red sharpie proved that to me one morning on the corner of Main and Walnut.

Made in the USA
Middletown, DE
30 November 2017